Of old in Rosamond's
Bower,
With its peacock hedges
of yew,
One could never find
the flower
Unless one was given
the clue;

So take the key of the
wicket,
Who would follow my
fancy free,
By formal knot and
clipt thicket,
And smooth green
sward so fair to see.

The Boy Pipes to the Elves

This Journal of
Enchantment
belongs to

 # My Faery Name is

_____

I dedicate this Journal of
Enchantment
to

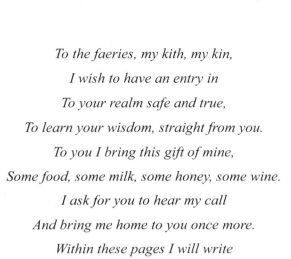

To the faeries, my kith, my kin,
I wish to have an entry in
To your realm safe and true,
To learn your wisdom, straight from you.
To you I bring this gift of mine,
Some food, some milk, some honey, some wine.
I ask for you to hear my call
And bring me home to you once more.
Within these pages I will write
Of magick, wonder, faery delight.
With each word my heart shall sing
And open wide, within this faery ring.

Faery

A JOURNAL OF ENCHANTMENT

Welcome to a faery ring, a magickal world between the worlds, your own enchanted journal. When you begin to write within these pages, something remarkable will begin to take place. With every stroke of the pen, you will be opening the doors between the worlds. With every word you write, you will be welcomed deeper and deeper into the blessed realm of Faerie—a land of legend, of myth, of faraway stone circles, forests, and castles of ancient lands. Yet in truth, the faery world is as close to you as the nearest plant, stone, tree, or field of flowers—or indeed, this very journal you now hold between your hands.

For the faeries are with every living creature, and are of each of the elements. They have been here since before time began, and are of the celestial and terrestrial spheres. They are known by many names: the Tylweth Teg, the Tuatha dé Danann, the Menahune, the devas, the djinn, the Seelie and Unseelie courts, the good folk, the sidhe—and many rumours and lies have been told of their powers and their intentions by those who envied them their ability to make the green world spring to life, to cleanse the waterways, to nurture and heal the animals, to love, dance, and heal the humans. And so we humans have distanced ourselves from them, feeling they are creatures of storybooks and fancy, or dangerous and untrustworthy. But the truth is they are as real as the natural world—beings of natural harmony, creativity, protection, growth, magick, love, and laughter.

The realm of Faerie has bright gifts to offer every living being. When you explore their magick and reclaim their gifts within this Journal of Enchantment, you will become more grounded, sensual, powerful, compassionate, clear, psychic, and in communion and harmony with all creation!

Do you wish to discover more? To fully enter the world of Faerie? To be offered their blessings, their magickal gifts?

Then all you need to do is write—and let all the wonder within you begin to live upon the page.

Do not worry about "what" to write, or "how" to write it down. This is a journal for enchanted explorations—and if you ever feel stuck, just ask the faeries for their assistance. Faeries can capture the imagination, inspire us to live lives where our intent and our actions are clear and strong, and help us to bring sensuality, power, and compassion into our lives. And they love helping us to explore our true selves and our creativity—just as they have been helping writers and magickal folk for thousands of years. They wish to help you, too, explore your dreams and visions through this journal.

The faeries work such bright magick—and through writing and exploring in this enchanted journal, you will learn how to create, direct, and channel this beautiful energy safely, responsibility, powerfully into your everyday life.

Be still ... breathe. Let the chatter of the mind grow faint, then quiet, and soft. Make room for the fae to enter.... And begin to look about you with the eyes of the faeries. Feel with the heart of the faeries. Know with the wisdom of the faeries. And let the part of you that is pure magick begin to be expressed with their help, in these most magickal pages.

They say in the old tales that if we do not believe in faeries, they die. But I do not believe this. If we do not believe in faeries, it is not that they perish ... but that a part of our soul dies and fades away, and the magick of life stays just out of reach, when it would often help us most....

For most of us, modern life does not always offer us imagination and beauty. It often encourages us to be productive and sensible and staid and sure, and sometimes it seems to ask us to dull all of our intuitive gifts. This is where this journal, and the faeries, can come in. Because here, in your own Journal of Enchantment, you will not be encouraged to be those things. Oh, no! Within this space, you can be as wild, and delightful, and full of daring, whimsy, and imagination as you wish. You can take flight, and dance, and grow your wings, wear the faery crown, and watch sparks fly from your faery wand, right here, within this Journal of Enchantment.

You see, faeries are real, and we can learn how to see them, feel their power, heal with them, and create a wonderful life by learning the secrets of working with the beautiful energy of these nature spirits and guardians! These powerful natural beings have been on the planet since the earth was born, and have been working with we humans for a very long time. Now we are at a turning point in our relationship—the closer we get to fae-reality, the more in touch we shall be with our own true nature, and to this beautiful planet!

For thousands of years, humans and faeries have lived alongside each other, sometimes harmoniously, sometimes in great fear and mistrust. In these times of magickal change and energetic evolution, it is more important than ever before to connect with our faery kith and kin! For from them we can discover the secrets to laughter, love, and living long healthy lives overflowing with purpose and joy.

This journal contains many blessings direct from the realm of Faerie, inspirational offerings of poetry and beauty from creative beings who saw and believed in the magick of faeries. I know their words will bring you enjoyment, enrichment and enchantment.

There are also many offerings from my own journals of enchantment—musings and thoughts from my own adventures within Faerie, and they are included here to support your own adventures into this most wondrous of realms, most magickal of paths.

Make this book your very own faery ring, a circle of bright magick, a kind of doorway into the faery realm. This is truly your very own Journal of Enchantment—the most important, most magickal words within it will be those you will place upon the page. This is the book of your thoughts and explorations, and your questions to the faeries. I know that by having one safe and magickal place to explore the wonders of Faerie, you can begin to reawaken the powers that I know lie deep within you, sweet human child.

You may wish to sketch your visions, or write a faery poem, or record dreams and wonders within these pages. You could explore your own relationship with nature, and add within each page a moment of faery magick that takes place for you each day. Let this be a faery ring, a safe and sacred place between the worlds where you record all the sweet moments that bring us back to Faerie—the spark of light from a tree, the whispers of beguiling voices, the soft chimes of faery bells, the moments when time changes and the world becomes fully alive and magickal and full of wonder once again. Never dismiss those moments.

In our modern world, we have become very enslaved to the consciousness of logic and rational thinking. Therefore, over time, we have slowly forgotten how to connect and tune in to Faerie. But we can all return, because the wonder of being alive, the connection to magick, lives deep within us, simply awaiting some time and some space and some attention. With time to daydream, to meander, to wander, to wonder, the magick is reignited and the world changes for us in wonderful ways.

So this journal is a place to begin on a most marvellous adventure—your own journey into the deep and wild wisdom of the faeries. Even if your days are spent far from a faery forest, and life is demanding and full of the mundane, this enchanted journal will provide you with a place of true magick and delight, where you can not so much escape from the real world, but return to what is most real and most necessary—the magick and wonder of being alive.

Let the words awaken your own wisdom. Let the beauty of the images awaken your imagination. Whisper the words out loud—like a prayer. They can open the doors between the worlds, and before long, your dreams, your imagination, your life force, your creativity, your heart, your wondrous, shining soul will be returned to its true state of enchantment and wonder.

May you rediscover your magick, and the faery within you, dear friend.

May you believe.

Lucy Cavendish

To be faery is to be a series of contradictions: it is to be noble and unstudied, natural and dignified, elegant and covered in earth, full of laughter but utterly serious all at once—and to change between all of these in the blink of an eye.

Too many humans impose again and again their opinions, even their energy, on a world they are reluctant to understand. If only we can begin to open up and accept the nature of the Faerie without our conditioning and expectation continually tainting the messages, we will do better than we have done before.

To be faery is to live fully, drink deeply, and invite sensuality and conviction into your life on a daily basis. It is to live without putting out that bright spark, that raw essential self that society can sometimes seek to bury, dim or be ashamed of.

When the lands of Faerie and the human world entwine, all is
empowered and made more beautiful. The human world becomes more
ensouled, and the missing pieces of our broken hearts are found again
in the simplest and sometimes the most powerful of ways. For the
faeries, I cannot speak, but it would seem to me that, if we have been
able to do so much harm, we must be able to bring solutions, creative
and compassionate, in their place.

Faery magick, in its wildness and in its wisdom, is shamanic in its nature: something wild and unbroken in it brings us what we — what our true self needs — which is not always what we think we want.

We faery folk are everywhere. We all play our part, and we have earned our place here at the table, with its feast of spirituality, as we are old, and the very bones upon which other faiths hang their clothes.

I have seen the brilliance of faery performers, who draw the veil away and bring the worlds closer. I have seen the sowers of seed, who grow back the green world. I have heard the faery shamans, who take us deep below and urge us to climb high in skeleton trees to find the keys to knowledge.

When we wear flowers in our hair, or representations of flowers, on a magickal level, our thoughts are as a garden—perfumed, natural, wild, and often beautiful. We are also "crowning" ourselves, and in that crowning, we acknowledge our own queen-nature, the sense that we are the sovereigns in our worlds.

_____
_____
_____
_____
_____
_____
_____
_____
_____
_____
_____
_____
_____
_____
_____
_____
_____
_____

They hold their great balls in the open air, in what is called a fairy ring. For weeks afterward you can see the ring on the grass. It is not there when they begin, but they make it by waltzing round and round. Sometimes you will find mushrooms inside the ring, and these are fairy chairs that the servants have forgotten to clear away. The chairs and the rings are the only tell-tale marks these little people leave behind them, and they would remove even these were they not so fond of dancing that they toe it till the very moment of the opening of the gates.

—J.M. Barrie, *Peter Pan*

or those who are awake and aware, for the faery people and the old ones, for the new souls being born, faeries create a sense that there is a place for the fragile. And because a faery will rarely live alone, they are a cure for our isolation and loneliness.

It is said that we humans can be reborn as faeries—if it is our time to experience this magickal form and energy ... but it is also said that if we do incarnate as a faery, it will be a long, long time before we incarnate again in another form. Perhaps this truth has given rise to the idea of being "trapped" in Faeryland—it is that the form and the energy is long and enduring, compared to the brief candlelight that is the human span of years.

Faerie is where the folklore and laws are held. Within the stories and the knowledge are the tales of seasons, walking between worlds, the wisdom of flowers and herb healing, the discovery of creativity, and the dangers of seduction.

THE MOON-MIST QUEEN AND
"LITTLE BOY."

Litha is the feast of the faery folk, and at this time, the doors between the worlds open, and we can peek through and dwell for just a little time in the otherworld of the faeries—a place where youth is everlasting, and enchantment plenty, and beauty, love, and joy are ours for all time.

At Summer Solstice, the shaman known as Santa soars high on the herbal power of fly agaric, female reindeers bring us gifts, and for a little while we can take pleasure in giving and receiving and being loving and sharing food, once again. That's a good day to have, whatever we call it—a faery day, a magick day. So, whatever you call it, enjoy a time of love and giving and the magick of the Solstice.

Tonight may be one of those amazing nights of clear communication, faery voices coming through and swirling on the warm air, clear and strong.... Head outside for a moment. Whisper to the faery queen and see what magick emerges from the sweetness of night.

When midsummer comes, there are blessings to all! A day and a night filled with sweet delights.... A time to allow yourself freedom and fun, wishes and wonders, as the veil thins and the fae folk dance in!

On midsummer night's eve, we are all dreaming in the love, the joy, the blessed outpouring of warmth and illumination from the height of the sun! Blessings to all to the north, as midwinter's icy darkness is pierced by the light, and blessings to the south, amidst this faery and flowered radiance.... Bright strong love to us all, at this sacred time!

Reshaping, recreating my altar, as the wheel turns towards the solstice time ... feathers and flowers and water and fire, antlered faery beings of stone and tree, shining shells and quiet bones of deep of sea, all of these are now set free as the sun continues her climb to that place in the sky we call the point of high stillness....

If we wish to connect with Faerie, we would do well to cast a magick circle, for a circle is a time between times, a world between worlds, a place where the fae, human, the old ones, and plant beings are one and together. Within the circle we can make a bright wish to cast into the cauldron.... I ask each of you to make this wish into our faery cauldron!

Faeries love gift giving, all year around. They are so generous. They help us to create an expansion of gratitude, to feel safe enough to offer our friendship and well wishes, to be there for each other. They remind us that we are here to truly love each other.

When faeries are about, you will feel the doors between the worlds widening, and joy and desire sweep through your world. Take a moment to feel the elation of Faeryland, and, if you wish, welcome in the faeries!

And so midsummer's eve begins, warm and soft and enchanted....
Blessings of the bright solstice, of the golden one, graceful and
sensuous the dance of Grian, wild the magicks of faery and healing, and
perfumed with flowers the sweet honey of the season! Fertile, sweetest
time, begin! Blessings of gold and longest light to us all in the south! A
blessing on us all!

Sweet Litha—can feel the doors between the worlds widening, and the joy, the fae, and the desire sweeping through the world... take a moment today to feel the joy of this season, and welcome in the faeries!

*Inspirations offered to the cauldron, Awen's gift sees forms emerge....
What are your hopes, dreams, and plans? What will you bring to birth
and offer the world? Ask the faeries for their help—and if you are a
true faery friend, you will have their most enchanted assistance.*

May you be gifted with health, wisdom, a life that is your own, true friends, laughter, family, connection, sensuality, pleasure, great love, honour, a planet in bloom and balance, and ecstatic union with the Divine.

*The gifts of the faery come through the plants and the flowering world.
The foods we eat, the things that we put into our bodies create "nwyfre"
(noo-wee-fray)—a connection to the eternal wheel of life, our direct
connection to the faeries.*

Over and above, people who deny the planet's offerings to them can run the risk of living in a permanent state of dissatisfaction and ingratitude. Faeries rarely appear to them, as they are waiting for their hearts to reopen to the potential of healing and joy.

We have never been so ruthlessly subjected to a culture that says we can purchase who we want to be. Faeries are puzzled by us, when all we need do is adorn ourselves with our own magick, believe in our own wonder, and awaken to the beauty of the world we share with so many amazing beings.

The animals that are most often associated with faerie — and with signs the otherworld is breaking through — are white animals. There has been a proliferation of white animals over the last forty years — acknowledged as heralds of a new era. Could the white animals also be ushering in a return of the faery folk?

Water horses are thought to dwell within lakes and ponds and in tidal pools. These faery steeds were so beautiful that humans would become entranced by the sight of the waterfae riding them, and would attempt to bridle them, ride them, tame them. Unable to hold on to them, as they were made of waves and light and air and foam, the humans would often drown, and the water horses were blamed for this. But in time, there came to be people who could ride the water horses—the people who watched, and learned from the faeries!

Faery animals are often great allies to the human folk. There is said to be a great sparkling white swan, a magickal faery bird that prophesies wild weather at Sennen Cove in Cornwall. And even now, this faery swan will send great sparks of light from the shore and the coves, like a faery light house, alerting the sea peoples of foul storms to come.

*Some say there are faery dogs that are black. Dubbed "wist hounds",
they are spectral creatures who form and reform, like rolling dark mists
across the landscape, and are said to hunt human souls. This I do not
know, and never have I seen them, but they are predatory, and may take
energy from those who observe them.*

Cows are sacred to the faery—and they have their own lovely faery cows, too, one of whom is called the freckled faery cow! She is loving and generous and brings pure, faery-blessed milk to humans, and she blesses their own herd with plenteous milk, long, happy lives, and fertility. If she—or her cows—are not honoured, or if her milk is taken by force, she retreats to a deep lake in Wales. She returns when she feels the new souls treating her lovely cattle with kindness and respect once again.

The Goddess Brigid is whispered to be part of the fae, and one of her symbols is the white cow—perhaps a faery cow!

Faeries have four forms that I've been blessed to see so far— a "humanoid" faery form, an animal form, a plant or flower form, and a light body, which is almost made of luminous sparks. They can shift between these forms, yet their essence remains the same.

Being with a Pooka (a mercurial-mooded house faery) is a little like living with a surly teenager. They can be withdrawn and difficult, and they love pranks, but they often then assist you with unexpected financial windfalls, startling, sudden wisdom, delightful whimsy, outbursts of joy, and great good fortune.

Faeries can be fierce beyond our imagining in their protection of their loved ones, their bloodline, and their spiritual home on the planet.

Faery cats have a certain look to their otherworldy eyes—a sense that they are drawing you in, inviting you to enter another world. And, indeed, they may be! It was long believed, in the enchanted highlands of Scotland, that if you gazed into the eyes of a cat sidhe that you, dear friend, would enter Faeryland.

Bone to bone,
Vein to vein,
Balm to balm,
Sap to sap,
Skin to skin,
Tissue to tissue,
Blood to blood,
Flesh to flesh,
Sinew to sinew,
Marrow to marrow,
Pith to pith,
Fat to fat,
Membrane to membrane,
Fibre to fibre,
Moisture to moisture.

——Healing chant of Airmid, the
faery goddess of plant and herbal
healing of Ireland

Plant thyme, for it will invite the faeries in. And along with the enchanted ones shall come the wondrous power of everlasting life, youth, vitality and joy.

Have you ever seen a little ring of mushrooms, or flowers forming a pretty circle? These are their meeting places. The circle is their place to talk. To discuss. To dance and rejoice! And if you see one, faery realms have touched your world, and you know you have been blessed!

"Sligh", from which "seelie" is derived, is Scots Gaelic for "bright and delightful, joyous", and is also the root of the word "silly". Think of that next time someone calls you silly. You may be simply sparkling with faery luminosity! Stay bright and shining, silly, wise, wonderful faery!

If you have a drop of the blessed faery blood, you can and will see and experience the fair folk. If they are not in your ancestry this lifetime, they may be more difficult to connect with, and your faery interactions may seem a little like straining to hear music carried on the wind. But anyone, with loving practice, can begin to sense them all about, whatever ancestry and DNA you may carry.

There are nine faery virtues, and there are seven faery gifts. Faery virtues are honesty, justice, compassion, courage, hope, faith, integrity, laughter, and joy. Faeries are generous, believe in free will, have strong ethics, are patient and peaceful, demonstrate great kindness and a hearty, passionate love of life.

The fae do not quite die, ever. They simple fade, their shimmer growing less and less bright over time, their energy being reabsorbed into the world of nature....

Recently, my faery friends tell me, fae such as the brownies and the goblins of homes have recognised they need to infiltrate places where people actually are these days! So, they have taken up residence more firmly in our workplaces and day care centres, as sometimes the people or children they need to reach and influence are spending less and less time at home, and more and more time at work.

Throughout the places where the veils between the worlds are thin, and through the gateways of the eight sacred festivals, come thundering the faery horses of the Wild Hunt. A-riding in their midst are queens and kings and lords and ladies of the Seelie and Unseelie courts. At their head is Gwynn ap Nudd. In front of them flies the White Hart, their quarry, and they ride on and on, through homes, and cities, and towns, never stopping.

The Wild Hunt is a faery activity that may rarely be seen, but it is one which always inspires awe. It is not a faery activity of recreation or play, but of the dynamic chase 'tween dark and light, of the changing of the seasons, and of the urge to seek out the sacred and to remind the planet that her sacred paths are being cleared and kept well.

They are said to have aristocratical Rulers and Laws, but no discernible religion.

—Robert Kirk, *The Secret Commonwealth,* 1691

He is no less a personage than the King of Faerie.... Very numerous indeed are his subjects and very various are they in nature. He is the sovereign of those beneficent and joyous beings ... who dance in the moonlight.

—Lady Charlotte Guest, *The Mabinogion*

Fairy, I am called, Gwyn the son of Nudd, the lover of Creurdylad, the daughter of Ludd....

—Gwynn ap Nudd, *The Black Book of Caemarthen,* 1250 AD

*If you wish to see the faeries, tuck an oak leaf or a four-leafed clover
inside your left shoe.*

The wall is silence,
The grass is sleep,
And the Fairy of Dreams
With moth-wings furled
Plays soft on her flute
To the drowsy world.

— Ida Rentoul Outhwaite, *Fairyland*

Wearing a green cloak or robe, or moss-coloured ribbons in your braided hair, will let the faeries know you are no foe, but a true friend.

Wherever is love and loyalty, great purposes, and lofty souls, even though in a hovel or a mine, there is Fairyland.

—Charles Kingsley

Faeries will do interesting things in the modern workplace: they will work on switching off the air-conditioning systems, turning off fluorescent lights, and setting off fire alarms, to give everyone some time spent outside in the natural light.

If we opened our minds to enjoyment,
We might find tranquil pleasures about us on every side.
We might live with the angels that visit on every sunbeam,
And sit with the faeries that wait on every flower.

—Samuel Smiles

The faeries of Ghana squeeze the juice of a sacred plant into the eyes, for the Sight, into the ears, to hear all, and into the mouth, to speak the language of the faeries, and sing the songs, creating harmony between the humans and the faeries once again.

And I serve the fairy queen,
To dew her orbs upon the green....
Farewell, thou lob of spirits; I'll be gone:
Our queen and all our elves come here anon.

—William Shakespeare, *A Midsummer Night's Dream*

*Enchanted worlds exist because the child within us never dies.
The doorways may be more obscure, but we can still seek them out.
There are still trees that speak and caverns that lead to nether realms.
There will always be faeries and elves within nature because they will
always be dancing within our hearts.*

—Ted Andrews, shaman and author

After falling asleep in a forest or upon a faery mound, a human would connect with the faeries and learn which herbs treat which ailments. The secrets of faery touch and healing can also be passed on in these connections.

Until she came into the land of faery,
Where nobody gets old and godly and grave,
Where nobody gets old and crafty and wise,
Where nobody gets old and bitter of tongue;
And she is still there, busied with a dance.
Deep in the dewy shadow of a wood,
Or where stars walk upon a mountain top.

—W.B. Yeats, *The Land of Heart's Desire*

_____
_____
_____
_____
_____
_____
_____
_____
_____
_____
_____
_____
_____
_____
_____
_____

Faeries sweet and faeries wild,
Come to visit me, your child.
Let me know when you're about.
Tell me stories to banish doubt.
All about me circle 'round,
Treasured memories once more found.
Faeries sweet and faeries wild,
Come and play with me, your child.

What the Young Man Saw in the Wood

Faeries, come take me out of this dull world,
For I would ride with you upon the wind,
Run on the top of the dishevelled tide
And dance upon the mountains like a flame.

—W.B. Yeats, *The Land of Heart's Desire*

Hand in hand, with faery grace,
Will we sing and bless this place.

— William Shakespeare, *A Midsummer Night's Dream*

*To pass their lives on fountains and on flowers
And never know the weight of human hours.*

—Lord Byron, *"Extracts from Don Juan: Haidée and Juan"*

The iron tongue of midnight hath told twelve:
Lovers, to bed; 'tis almost faery time.

—William Shakespeare, *A Midsummer Night's Dream*

I think that people who can't believe in faeries aren't worth knowing.

—Tori Amos

Princess Edane heard a voice singing on a May Eve like this, and followed half awake and half asleep, until she came into the Land of Faery....

—W.B. Yeats, *The Land of Heart's Desire*

I call to thee, my faery guide,
To allow me to see thee,
Speak with thee,
Know thee.

I do believe in fairies, I do, I do.

—J.M. Barrie, *Peter Pan*

Tink was not all bad: or, rather, she was all bad just now, but, on the other hand, sometimes she was all good. Fairies have to be one thing or the other, because being so small they unfortunately have room for one feeling only at a time. They are, however, allowed to change, only it must be a complete change.

—J.M. Barrie, _Peter Pan_

It is frightfully difficult to know much about the fairies, and almost the only thing for certain is that there are fairies wherever there are children.

—J.M. Barrie, *"Peter Pan Lock-out Time"*

There may be fairies at the bottom of the garden. There is no evidence for it, but you can't prove that there aren't any, so shouldn't we be agnostic with respect to fairies?

—Richard Dawkins

*Blind folk see the fairies.
Oh, better far than we,
Who miss the shining of their wings
Because our eyes are filled with things
We do not wish to see.*

—Rose Fyleman, *Fairies and Chimneys*

Deaf folk hear the fairies,
However soft their song;
'Tis we who lose the honey sound
Amid the clamour all around
That beats the whole day long.

—Rose Fyleman, *Fairies and Chimneys*

The one thing I always wanted was to see a fairy story come true. I am living in a fairy story. I feel as if I might be a fairy myself, and able to turn things into anything else.

—Frances Hodgson Burnett

Fairies, black, grey, green, and white,
You moonshine revellers and shades of night,
You orphan heirs of fixed destiny,
Attend your office and your quality.

—William Shakespeare, *The Merry Wives of Windsor*

Faerie is a perilous land, and in it are pitfalls for the unwary and dungeons for the overbold.... The realm of fairy-story is wide and deep and high and filled with many things: all manner of beasts and birds are found there; shoreless seas and stars uncounted; beauty that is an enchantment, and an ever-present peril; both joy and sorrow as sharp as swords. In that realm a man may, perhaps, count himself fortunate to have wandered, but its very richness and strangeness tie the tongue of a traveller who would report them. And while he is there it is dangerous for him to ask too many questions, lest the gates should be shut and the keys be lost.

—J.R.R. Tolkien

F. RICHARDSON

As Beren looked into her eyes,
Within the shadows of her hair,
The trembling starlight of the skies,
He saw there mirrored shimmering.
Tinuviel, the elven-fair,
Immortal maiden, elven-wise,
About him cast her shadowy hair
And arms like silver glimmering.

*—*J.R.R. Tolkien, *The Lord of the Rings*

The leaves were long, the grass was green,
The hemlock-umbels tall and fair,
And in the glade a light was seen
Of stars in shadow shimmering.
Tinuviel was dancing there
To music of a pipe unseen,
And light of stars was in her hair,
And in her raiment glimmering.

—J.R.R. Tolkien, *The Lord of the Rings*

I believe when I am in the mood that all nature is full of people whom we cannot see, and that some of these are ugly or grotesque, and some wicked or foolish, but very many beautiful beyond any one we have ever seen, and that these are not far away ... the simple of all times and the wise men of ancient times have seen them and even spoken to them.

—W.B. Yeats

*Fairies in Ireland are sometimes as big as we are, sometimes bigger,
and sometimes, as I have been told, about three feet high.*

—W.B. Yeats

In emerald tufts, flowers purple, blue and white;
Like sapphire, pearl, and rich embroidery,
Buckled below fair knighthood's bending knee;
Fairies use flower for their charactery.

—William Shakespeare, *The Merry Wives of Windsor*

Once upon a time, I thought faeries lived only in books, old folktales, and the past. That was before they burst upon my life as vibrant, luminous beings, permeating my art and my everyday existence, causing glorious havoc.

—Brian Froud

Ah, faeries, dancing under the moon,
A Druid land, a Druid tune!
While still I may, I write for you
The love I lived, the dream I knew.

—W.B. Yeats, *To Ireland in the Coming Times*

Cherries of the night are riper
Than the cherries pluckt at noon
Gather to your fairy piper
When he pipes his magic tune:
Merry, merry,
Take a cherry;
Mine are sounder,
Mine are rounder,
Mine are sweeter
For the eater
Under the moon.
And you'll be fairies soon.

—Robert Graves, *Cherry-Time*

No child but must remember laying his head in the grass, staring into the infinitesimal forest and seeing it grow populous with fairy armies.

—Robert Louis Stevenson

Wind chimes in your yard will serenade garden creatures—squirrels, fairies and angels.

—Author unknown

There never was a merry world since the fairies left off dancing and the Parson left conjuring.

—John Seldon

Any man can lose his hat in a fairy-wind.

—Irish proverb

I'll seek a four-leaved shamrock
In all the faery dells,
And if I find the charmed leaves,
Oh how I'll weave my spells!

—Samuel Lover, *The Four-Leaved Shamrock*

Once we have encountered Faerie, no matter if we choose our humanity over our magick, we are never the same. We are forever changed, and forever better because of our knowledge of Faerie.

Faeries live outside of chronological time—faery time is different, and faery beings can bend and shift time, even travelling through epochs to reappear at just the right moment.

Humans with the enchanted blood often suffer addictions until they find other ways to penetrate the veil and to handle the density and difficulty of being a little more human than they are faery.

Faeries change appearance frequently. While their essence remains the same, the way it is perceived shifts entirely. Faery people often morph again and again, yet remain utterly themselves and utterly captivating.

People with the faery blood are lightning rods for magick: in-between creatures who split the grey world, break open our hearts, widen our minds, and penetrate our souls with rare and delightful enchantments.

There are, in this world currently dominated by illusory humans, people threaded through with a rare combination of stardust and faery glamour, people who are "other", who have a luminous quality. They shine—the Shining Ones.

Gnomes are faeries who are often overlooked. Perhaps 'tis because they dwell down so deep within the earth. They are very strong beings — they offer inspiration that is so grounded and achievable that they can almost seem like very solid counsellors, rather than elementals. They are particularly helpful for people who tend to be unable to choose or who find it difficult to settle and focus.

The fae of the underworlds, the gnomes, intuitively guide us to create lasting wealth, the kind that endures, and can help us to find homes, inheritance, and value in the land. Gnomes, more than any other elemental, reveal to us the practical processes that need to take place in order for us to bring our visions into the material plane in an abiding fashion. They are about legacy.

_____

_____

_____

_____

_____

_____

_____

_____

_____

_____

_____

_____

_____

_____

_____

_____

_____

_____

_____

_____

_____

_____

Faeries communicate with we humans very clearly—and nearly all the time. It is simply a matter of tuning into their world and beginning to read the signs for ourselves—and sense their energy about us, within the world, and sometimes within our own blood. Their signs and their messages are always very clear and very sweet. However, people who have not developed their intuition or their sensitivity seem to be quite blind or immune to the faery signs and the faery healing magicks that are everywhere!

Insects, like cicadas, ladybirds, Christmas beetles, dragonflies, and butterflies, all work alongside the faeries and have fascinating arrangements. Some are faerie steeds, and have a close and very bonded relationship with the faeries! Bees too are a wonderful sign of faery activity and natural health!

Faeries tell me they are puzzled at the source of some of our great unhappinesses, as we say we want certain things, we humans, but we often do not see all the beauty around us, and are very destructive. So, when we wish to ask the faeries a question, please be sure to consider their world, first of all. Faeries value the natural world, gratitude, courage, laughter, sweetness, healing, and fun!

Thyme is perhaps the most magickal and powerful of all herbs in terms of attracting and drawing loving faery helpers. Thyme faeries make a safe haven for all other faeries to visit you. By growing this herb, you also invite the faeries to work with and cleanse your own energetic body. This is because thyme raises your vibration and assists you in feeling connected to other dimensions, allowing all to flow, and helping you understand and merge with concepts that are outside of logic and linear time—like the faeries themselves!

There are many winged messengers of the fae. When I was little, my message from the black prince cicadas was to work hard at what I wanted to learn and have friends to help me. The "green grocers", as I called the green cicadas, told me to water my plants and eat more green, bright foods, and the yellow cicadas told me to have more sunlight!

Faery hounds and dogs: the Wild Hunt and a time of cleansing, is very powerful! If you should see a faery hound with the Wild Hunt, check to see if they have red ears! They are a very powerful sign that change is coming.

Faeries are not simply sweet little flower creatures. They are that, but they can also be large, wild, essential, deep, fierce, and above all, primal and natural, dignified and elegant.

At every moment in our lives, we have one foot in a fairy tale and the other in the abyss.

—Paulo Coelho.

Just living is not enough, said the Butterfly Faerie. One must have sunshine, freedom, and a little flower.

—Hans Christian Anderson, *The Complete Fairy Tales*

How featly they trip it! how happy are they
Who pass all their moments in frolic and play,
Who rove where they list, without sorrows or cares,
And laugh at the fetters mortality wears!

—Carolina Eliza Scott, *The Fairy Dance*

The moonlight fades from flower and rose
And the stars dim one by one;
The tale is told, the song is sung,
And the Fairy feast is done.
The night-wind rocks the sleeping flowers,
And sings to them, soft and low.
The early birds erelong will wake:
'Tis time for the Elves to go.

—Louisa May Alcott, *Fairy Song*

Egg-shells are favourite hidey-homes of the faeries. A gentle wash in pure water, and pop one or two into the garden, and your faeries will make a sweet bed in which to rest when they tire of their dance and labours.

Finvarra, the king of the fairies of the west, is said to keep the most friendly relations with the ancient families of Galway, especially the Kirwans of Castle Hacket. Finvarra is a gentleman faery, "every inch of him", it is said, and so the Kirwans leave for him kegs of the finest wine. In return, Finvarra is said to have blessed this old family with enviable and mysterious abundance.

Being elemental, the way in which the faeries communicate with we humans can take many forms, some of which may seem unusual for those of us used to the more direct forms of communication humans tend to prefer. Their messages are whispered on the wind, transmitted through intuitive feelings and hunches, and seen in magickal visions.

The faeries can reach out to us by calling us to a place, creating a faery ring near our home, and by ringing soft chimes that we can only just barely hear, but once heard, can never forget.

There has long been exchange and communication between the worlds of human and faery. And when the veils lift, as they do at the borders of day and light, or spring and summer, or the day of longest light, they will appear to us, and we can receive their blessings, their teachings, their magick.

Faeries have long been feared by humans. But the truth is they have far more to fear from us, than we from them.

Faeries come to you when you pause between the rush and hurry of the day and gaze upon the beauty of a flower, breathe in its scent, and take a moment to feel the blessings of nature that are, in truth, our greatest abundance.

Faeries can become as one with the tree or the flower or the fountain they have been made the protector of. And if that tree or flower or fountain is harmed, so too is the faery guardian of that place. If we speak to them of what we do—prune a shrub, remove a tree, or take some of the waters, they can have their moment to gather their energy and prepare. They will then offer us blessings, as we offer them respect and care in return.

Faeryland is a place of healing, magick, physical rebirth, and deep, wild connection. When we enter Faeryland, we must be open to changes, for they will come. A different destiny is for those who seek the blessings of Faerie.

Faeries bridge the celestial and the terrestrial, embodying and enspiriting all that is best and gladdest of heaven and of earth.

When we begin to reweave our relationship with the wild ones, the fae, we begin to reclaim our own abilities to heal, nurture, live with freedom and a kind of true courtesy, and respect to all the forms of life here on Gaia.

Faeries love what is within us, that brief bright spark of soulfire that burns so swiftly through the span of our years. We will grow old, and they remain ever-young. We can become unwell, and they dance and fly and leap. We can become sad and dark and bitter, but they, who are ever-young, do not. But when they come to us—and they will, sure as you are reading these words—all that is innocent and wild and pure within you will be awakened. You will drink the elixir from the grail, and when you do this, sweetness, vitality, fertility, and the springtime of your soul can be restored. We will become old and weary, but we will remember all of who we are, without rancour and bitterness, but with gratitude and delight.

That is the gift of faery. An everlasting freedom of spirit.

Glamour is the convergence of your highest self with your external appearance, the manifestation of personal power through form. It is a gift of the faeries, and can help us to show ourselves, who we truly are, when we most have need.

Those who push and hurry at the faeries to do their bidding and grant their wishes will rarely find what they seek. A faery is a wild thing, and wild things cannot be ordered, or rushed, or enslaved. We ask, and we let go. And the fae will return to us so much more than we could have ever imagined—in our waking life, and beyond, in the land of dreams where they can most often reach us with their blessed inspirations.

The faeries are swift, it is true, but for them to reach us, we must slow down, and listen, and simply be a while. Rest beneath a hawthorn tree, stay so still a butterfly lands upon you, feel the world alive and pulsing with brilliance, all about you. Soften and open, and there they are, in the fall of feather, the discovery of a special stone, a message in the shape of the clouds.

Faeries fall in love with humans all the time. They love our brief lives, our strong emotions, our energy, which is wild and strong. They love our solidity, the transient beauty of our youth, the wisdom of the best of us as we grow old. Once a faery loves us, they will often stay 'til the end of our days and love us when our beauty fades and life force dims. And when we love them too, we can then take our place among them, when our time as human is finally done.

Human time is a kind of enslavement. Faery time is free and vast and a little daunting, too. Enter into Faeryland, and time will expand and shift and offer up the potential we humans have robbed ourselves of. Safety is not the way of faery. Freedom is the flag they fly.

Gal-Grian (gull-greeahn): *A burst of energy from the Faery Goddess Grian, shooting forth new light into someone who has been hurt or wounded, like a burst of healing energy and golden light that can help us overcome even the most bloody and awful of wounds, both energetic and physical (and emotional and mental, too). The greatest burst of this is seen as Newgrange (named for Grian) each year at Winter Solstice.*

If you wish to grow the most delicious organic vegetables and fruit, the faeries can help you by shepherding insects and animals who may wish to feast on your produce away from the garden! Always thank the faeries, and you and they will have a mutually beneficial gardening arrangement!

When a faery wishes to protect you, you may see blue fire, like sparks of light about you.

Many fae, like the Tuatha dé Danann of Ireland, shapeshifted into the sacred land itself, and thus they house and hold the bones of our ancestors, and their wisdoms too.

Each plant has its own faery who weaves the sunlight into nutrients, who collects dew, and cradles the tender buds of the new born flowers ... all that grows ripens with their help. Thus, all we eat is faery food. When we chemically interfere with this process, the faery energy, the nwyfre, (noo-wee-fray) or life force within the plant, is diminished, and we lose our sight, our way, our own energy, our own nwyfre.

_____
_____
_____
_____
_____
_____
_____
_____
_____
_____
_____
_____
_____
_____
_____
_____
_____
_____
_____
_____
_____
_____
_____

You may have faery ancestors, your own faery blood. Allow the thoughts and feelings and message from your faery kith and kin to come through for you. Ask them for their advice and assistance in making the song of your fae blood become clearer and stronger, if this is what you wish to experience.

Faeries dwell between the unseen and the seen worlds, and they understand how to make visible what cannot always be seen with the eye, and what will not always be believed by the mind.

Fae beings love—they just do. They love us, despite humanity's reckless disregard for the natural world, our disregard even for our own good and happiness. They love, and do not hold grudges. They love us without a sense of attachment and ownership; they love us without demanding anything from us.

Faeries offer healing to animals, to plants wounded by pesticides and chemicals, to waterways bogged by rubbish, and to us. They can help heal our wounded hearts, if we allow them to. Simply offer some help to them, an offering in the form of clearing the natural world, and they will begin to work their magick upon you, if you let them in.

Faeries have a song: they sing the energy of the world into being. You too have a song, in harmony with the song of the world. Faeries love to hear you sing, to make sound, to find your voice, and express and share and be fully alive to the power of sound, which opens the worlds between the worlds.

The Celtic faeries, the Tuatha dé Danann and the Tylweth Teg, know that what some call a halo is simply the energetic field radiated by the fully-awakened crown chakra! Called "fire in the head", a person who glows with this faery fire is creative, able to manifest, radiantly attractive, and connected.

We humans often have a deep mistrust of our own power, because we have seen its misuse by others. We no longer trust ourselves. However, with the help of the fae, we can learn to work with our power in beautiful, responsible ways that bring creativity, joy, and generosity into our lives and into the lives of others.

The faery know that true power is the activation of life force in order to change the world and create within the world things of meaning and substance, beauty and goodness. True power is to understand the best ways in which to nurture your own talents and create the world in which you wish to live.

Faery Sight is not to be confused with hallucinations or visions that disrupt your safety — they can be played on your spirit eye region, without compromising your everyday eyesight. The gift of Faery Sight can help you to very clearly see the wonderment all around you — lifting the veil that makes everything "real" drab and ordinary, and revealing the exquisite beauty of life, the shining colour and bright glory of life in visual ways.

Faeries can be seen! A little pollen on the eyelids, a little honey in the nut, just one night beneath a faery tree ... and you will see the shining ones!

Faeries work with the healing arts of herb and touch, divination, manifestation, creativity, music, art, writing, and ecstatic, sensual rites. Their power and freedom caused the Church to forbid interaction with the faeries. But they never really left us—they await one sign, and we can re-enter this sacred alliance with the fair folk.

"Pagans", from the Latin word "paganus", for "country-dwellers", continued to respect and work with the faeries long after most humans were taught to fear and disrespect them. Those who danced under the moonlight with the fae were often called witches, and so faeries and witches alike were accused of terrible things, only some of which were true.

It is not silly or childish to be a believer in the fae. It is wise and open-hearted and wild, and will return to you a part of your soul, the wild innocence so many humans let go of once childhood ends.

As long as there are wild things, there will be faeries.

Whitethorn trees are said to be the resting place for the trouping faeries of Ireland—the faeries who travel and walk the energy lines of that magickal land.

In a faery place, a faery ring, time seems to slow. The air can become light and sweet, the sun shines and rainbows abound, but just outside the faery ring, rain will fall, and lightning can crack the sky.

People with a touch of faery blood are often outsiders—
they seem a little peculiar and different, and the world needs their
strange magick so very much!

The Unseelie Court are not so fond of humans—they feel we are dangerous and prideful. 'Tis up to us who are faery friends to show them the goodness that humans can have inside!

The Seelie Court still believe that humans can do good and be strong allies of the faeries and of the planet. It is up to those of us who are faery friends to show them we are indeed worthy of the great gift of their trust.

The Welsh faeries are called the Tylweth Teg and live in a land known as Tir na Og. They know great secrets, and their potions are the most powerful ever created!

It is said that faeries are afraid of iron—but they are not so much afraid of iron, as they are afraid of what we humans will do with iron—make machines that eat the earth, plunder her sacred caves of ore and crystal, and hurt one another, dreadfully. Some of the faeries are masters of smithcraft and metalwork—so do not say they fear iron. It is the humans and their capacity to harm with iron that they fret over.

Faeries are the weavers of Source, the energy which is wound into every flower, every tree and every sod of earth.

Ask the faeries to help you to change. They are in charge of transformation, the management of earth alchemy—and as they oversee the business of breaking down and re-creation, they can assist you to let go and to recreate your own magickal life.

Faeries seem dangerous to those who want their magick and their healing safe, orderly, and predictable. But the faeries are not so—and nor are you, not deep within your wild heart. You are made of slightly different stuff, but the essence of ecstasy flows through your veins too, human child.

Faeries often have long, lustrous and wild hair. Their locks are alive and sensitive, sensing energy and receiving messages like the most beautiful of antennae.

There are faeries in the great stone forests of man. They wear a disguise and are called dark faeries, for they wish to be known as fearful, even dangerous. They nurture the blades of grass and the tiny flowers that spring up between the cracks in the pavement, all the while reminding us that we can never bury nature's energy, not even with all our iron machinery and great forever. The dark faeries are sensitive and vulnerable, and they wear their camouflage and snarl and growl, for fear we will take away the very last drop of nature's power if we knew how fragile they truly are.

The faeries teach us that the world of the earth, the realm of all that grows and seeks the light of the sun, is precious and pure. They wish for you to accept and nurture your own natural form—your body—and in doing so, bring back that love and respect to all of nature and her children.

To be touched by the faeries is to have dreamed with eyes wide open. And once we have seen them, we cannot unsee them or lessen the enchantment. The whole of the world is changed, for we are the people the earth has been entrusted to, and the faeries ask us to rise and celebrate this beautiful planet.

Close your eyes for just a moment, and see yourself being sprinkled, from head to toe with shining faery dust. As this settles upon you, and you begin to sparkle and glow, catching the light with your brilliance, within you, a golden light starts to grow.

The faeries want you to know that love, falling in love, being in love, is a powerful energy that is your birthright. It is a sacred blessing, and one which can be experienced over and over — within a lifetime, within one relationship, if you allow the magick of belief and enchantment into your love.

All the children pleaded for the faeries, and said they were good friends and dear to them, and never did them any harm, but the priest would not listen, and said it was a sin and a shame to have such friends.

——Mark Twain, *Personal Recollections of Joan of Arc*

Faery faith always springs back to life, for its roots are deep and cannot be touched.

Every house and humble cottage has its brownie, its boggart, its domovoi, its lutin. You can explain away the mysterious things that take place as cleverly as you wish, but these strange and loving beings are right there, awaiting a little milk and honey from your favourite dish.

In Wales, it is said many a faery woman took a human man for her husband, and every member of those families, from then to this day, has the power of faery healing.

Witches were nearly always accused of consorting with the faeries, and thus they too were considered wicked and tricksy, but not much could be farther from the truth.

Faeries often bless us with a song.... One such song can be sung at a child's birth, and a person can seek the source of the song that haunts them their whole lives, not knowing it was a blessing from the fair folk, wishing them long life, endless peace, and delicious joy for every one of their days on the earth.

The Inuit people call faeries "aua". The aua bring to the tribes the knowledge of where to hunt, where to conduct ceremonies, and how to stay well in difficult times. They are described as tiny females, with pointed caps and dainty shoes, and to be no larger than a loaf of bread!

Some call the Seelie Court the "summer fae", or the "light fae". Some say they are immense and shining and crowned in dew-like jewels and garments of petal and feather. They are glorious, and hold pageants and balls that humans can join, in their dreams, or deep within a faery forest, on special nights when the Seelie clans gather and dance their magicks into the world.

If you make a promise to the faeries it would be wise to keep it, as they take very seriously the giving of word, pledges, and oaths. If you keep the promise, blessings aplenty shall be yours. They will not harm you should you not keep it, but they will not appear to you as they once did, or not for a very long time.

Safe haven is offered by the faeries to those who have won their trust. They can offer you the cloak of enchantment, to help you be less visible, or wrap you within their gossamer wings, and keep you safe from all about you.

You too can have faery wings. If ever you feel a tickling, a prickling between your shoulder blades, that is the very beginning of the growth of your wings, which cannot be seen with human eyes (except by those with the Sight).

Ask the faeries to help you find a special piece of fallen wood from a faery tree. This can be your very own magickal faery wand, which will draw energy lines, direct energy, and help you to charge other magickal objects.

You will often see faeries as a spark of light, a momentary flash from the very corner of your eye. Turn to stare and they will vanish—but keep your gaze soft and indirect, and they will soon let you see them more and more!

You have a faery name. Hidden within the letters of your own name, or deep within your memory, is a name the faeries gave to you when you were born, a special name to unlock the doors between the worlds. You can rediscover your own faery name—and when you do, your powers will grow threefold!

All flowers are magickal, and all flowers have their own faeries—but some will sing to you more than others. Bluebells were even called faery thimbles, foxgloves were faery petticoats, and lavender was once called elf leaf by the keepers of the old ways.

Make a little faery ring within your garden, using stones, or shells if you live by the sea, or plant thyme in a circle, or use crystals.... The faeries will know they then have a place to dance and to sing, and you will be blessed with their enchantment and energy for many days and nights to come!

The wild wisdom of the faeries is not a magickal practise for those who wish only for their will and power to manifest: we who walk the path of faery are choosing to ally ourselves with Nature, and it is Her will that will be done.

Faeries take on a great deal of the features of the land they dwell in ... mossy limbs, camouflage marking on their faces, hair that looks like feathers, or twisting strands of corn threads.

Faery blessings can reignite the magickal embers of faery fire that lie within you, simply awaiting you to allow yourself to shine once again—and to remember, finally, all of the luminous glory of your being.

MORGAN LE FAY CASTS AWAY THE SCABBARD